Tips for Reading Together

Children learn best when reading is fun.

- Talk about the title and the pictures on the cover.
- Look through the pictures together so your child can see what the story is about.
- Read the story to your child, placing your finger under the words as you read.
- Have fun finding the hidden robin.
- Read the story again and encourage your child to join in.
- Give lots of praise as your child reads with you.

Children enjoy reading stories again and again.
This helps to build their confidence.

Have fun!

Find the robin hidden in every picture.

The Snowman

Cynthia Rider • Alex Brychta

OXFORD
UNIVERSITY PRESS

Biff   Chip   Wilma

Wilf   Kipper   Floppy

Wilma made a snowman.

8

It had a red nose.

It had a blue scarf.

It had green gloves.

It had a black hat.

16

The hat fell on Floppy.

Floppy ran.

Oh no!

No snowman!

Think about the story

What are the colours the snowman is wearing?

Why did Floppy run off?

What else could you put on the snowman?

What would you like to make with snow or sand?

Fun activity

Find the twin snowmen.

**Useful common words repeated in this story and
other books at Level 1.**

a   had   it   no

Names in this story: Biff   Chip   Kipper   Wilf   Wilma   Floppy

More books for you to enjoy

Level 1: Getting Ready

Level 2: Starting to Read

Level 3: Becoming a Reader

Level 4: Building Confidence

Level 5: Reading with Confidence

OXFORD
UNIVERSITY PRESS

Great Clarendon Street,
Oxford OX2 6DP

Text © Cynthia Rider 2006
Illustrations © Alex Brychta 2006

First published 2006
All rights reserved

Series Editors: Kate Ruttle,
Annemarie Young

British Library Cataloguing
in Publication Data available

ISBN–13: 978-019-279224-2

10 9 8 7 6 5 4 3 2 1

Printed in China by Imago